EASIEST
KEYBOARD
COLLECTION

Latin

WISE PUBLICATIONS
London/New York/Paris/Sydney/Copenhagen/Madrid/Tokyo

Exclusive Distributors:

Music Sales Limited
8/9 Frith Street,
London W1V 5TZ, England.

Music Sales Pty Limited
120 Rothschild Avenue,
Rosebery, NSW 2018,
Australia.

Order No. AM955834
ISBN 0-7119-8278-3
This book © Copyright 2000 by Wise Publications

Compiled by Nick Crispin
Music arranged by Roger Day
Music processed by Paul Ewers Music Design

Printed in the United Kingdom by
Caligraving Limited, Thetford, Norfolk.

Cover photograph courtesy of Rex Features

Your Guarantee of Quality
As publishers, we strive to produce every book to the highest
commercial standards.
The music has been freshly engraved and the book has been carefully
designed to minimise awkward page turns and to make playing from
it a real pleasure.
Particular care has been given to specifying acid-free, neutral-sized
paper made from pulps which have not been elemental chlorine
bleached. This pulp is from farmed sustainable forests and was
produced with special regard for the environment.
Throughout, the printing and binding have been planned to ensure
a sturdy, attractive publication which should give years of enjoyment.
If your copy fails to meet our high standards, please inform us and
we will gladly replace it.

Music Sales' complete catalogue describes thousands of titles and is
available in full colour sections by subject, direct from Music Sales
Limited. Please state your areas of interest and send a cheque/postal
order for £1.50 for postage to: Music Sales Limited, Newmarket Road,
Bury St. Edmunds, Suffolk IP33 3YB.

www.musicsales.com

Contents

AMAPOLA

Words by Albert Gamse
Music by Joseph M. Lacalle

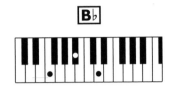  

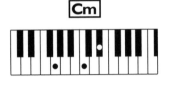 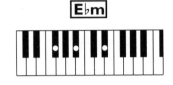 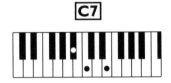

Voice: **Brass Ensemble**

Rhythm: **Fox Trot**

Tempo: ♩ = 144

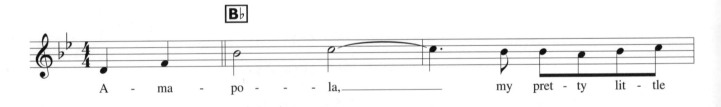

A - ma - po - - - la,——— my pret - ty lit - tle

pop - py,——— you're like that love - ly flow'r, so

sweet and hea - ven - ly. Since I

found you,——— my heart is wrapped a - round you,———

4

and lov - ing you, it seems to beat a

B♭

rhap - so - dy. A - ma - po - - la,_____

_____ the pret - ty lit - tle pop - py,_____ must co - py its en -

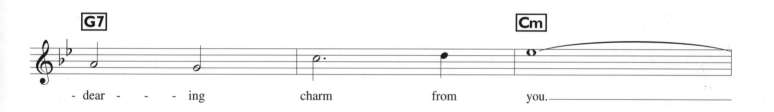

G7   **Cm**

- dear - - ing   charm   from   you._____

G7   **Cm**   **E♭m**

_____ A - ma - po - - la,_____   A - ma -

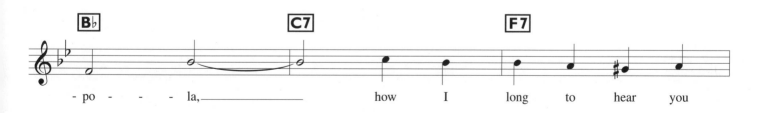

B♭   **C7**   **F7**

- po - - la,_____   how   I   long   to   hear   you

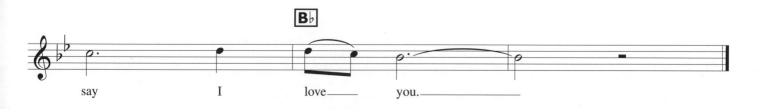

B♭

say   I   love_____   you._____

BAMBOLÉO

Words & Music by Tonino Baliardo, Nicolas Reyes, Jalhoul Bouchikhi & Simon Jose Diaz

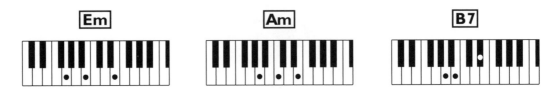

Voice: **Flute**

Rhythm: **Punta**

Tempo: ♩ = 142

Es - te a - mor lle - ga a - si es - ta ma - ne -

- ra   no tie - ne la cul -

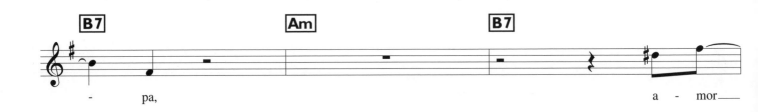

- pa,   a - mor____

____ de com - pre - men - ta,   a - mor del mes pa -

- sa - do,   bem - be - le,   bem - be - le,   bem - be - le,

bem,   bem - be - le,   bem - be - le.

Bam - bo - lé - o,_____

_____ bam - bo - lé - a,_____   por - qué mi

vi - da yo la pre - fie - ro vi - vir a - si._____

Bam - bo - lé - o,_____   bam - bo -

- lé - a,_____   por - qué mi vi - da yo la pre -

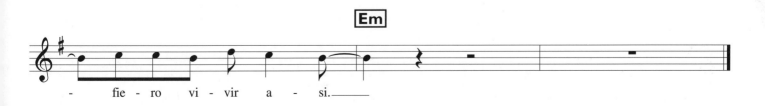

- fie - ro vi - vir a - si._____

BÉSAME MUCHO

Original Words & Music by Consuelo Velazquez
English Words by Sunny Skylar

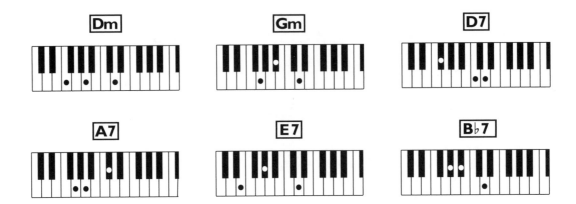

Voice: **Vibes**

Rhythm: **Cha-Cha**

Tempo: ♩ = 124

Bé - sa - me,____ bé - sa - me mu - cho.____

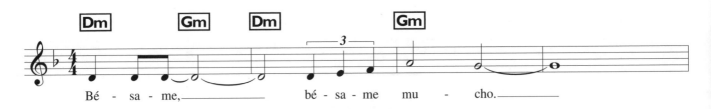

Each time I cling to your kiss, I hear mu - sic di - vine.____

Bé - - - - - sa - me mu - cho,____

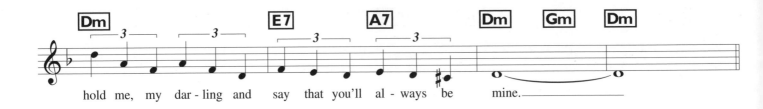

hold me, my dar - ling and say that you'll al - ways be mine.____

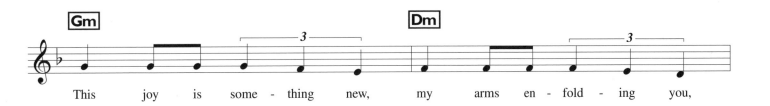

This joy is some - thing new, my arms en - fold - ing you,

ne - ver knew this thrill be - fore. Who - ev - er thought I'd be

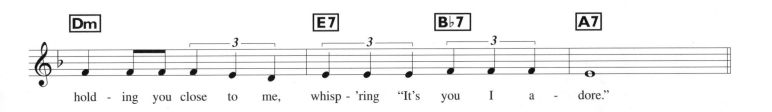

hold - ing you close to me, whisp - 'ring "It's you I a - dore."

Dear - est one,_____ if you should leave me,_____

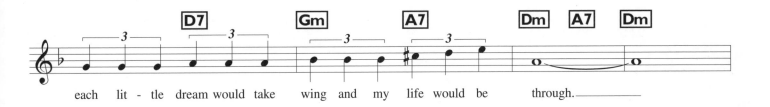

each lit - tle dream would take wing and my life would be through._____

Bé - - - - - - sa - me mu - cho,_____

love me for - ev - er and make all my dreams come true._____

CORCOVADO
(Quiet Nights Of Quiet Stars)

Original Words & Music by Antonio Carlos Jobim
English Words by Gene Lees & Buddy Kaye

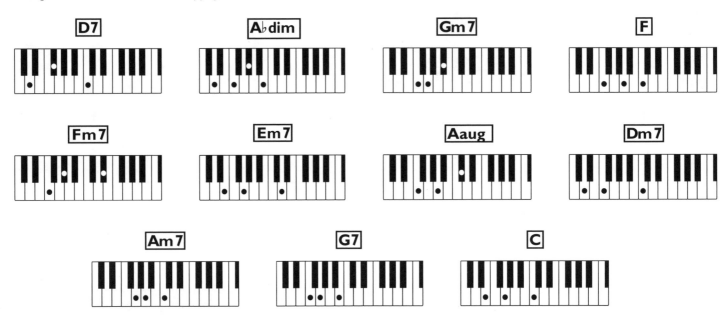

Voice: **Vibes**

Rhythm: **Bossa Nova**

Tempo: ♩ = 112

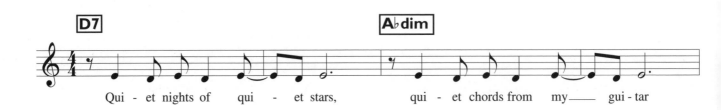

Qui - et nights of qui - et stars, qui - et chords from my ___ gui - tar

float - ing on the si - lence that ___ sur - rounds ___ us. ___

Qui - et thoughts and qui - et dreams, ___ qui - et walks by qui - et streams,

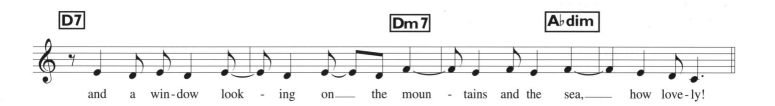

and a win-dow look - ing on the moun - tains and the sea, how love - ly!

This is where I want to be, here with you so close

to me un - til the fi - nal flick - er of life's em -

- ber. I, who was lost and

lone - ly, be - liev - ing life was on - ly.

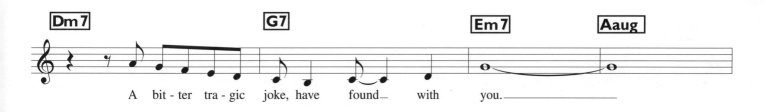

A bit - ter tra - gic joke, have found with you.

The mean - ing of ex - is - tence, oh my love.

DESAFINADO
(Slightly Out Of Tune)

Original Words by Newton Mendonca
Music by Antonio Carlos Jobim
English Words by Jon Hendricks & Jessie Cavanaugh
© Copyright 1959 Editora Musical Arapua, Brazil.
© Copyright 1962 with English words Hollis Music Incorporated, USA.
TRO Essex Music Limited, Suite 2.07, Plaza 535 Kings Road, London SW10
for the British Commonwealth (excluding Canada and Australasia)
and the Republics of Ireland and South Africa.
All Rights Reserved. International Copyright Secured.

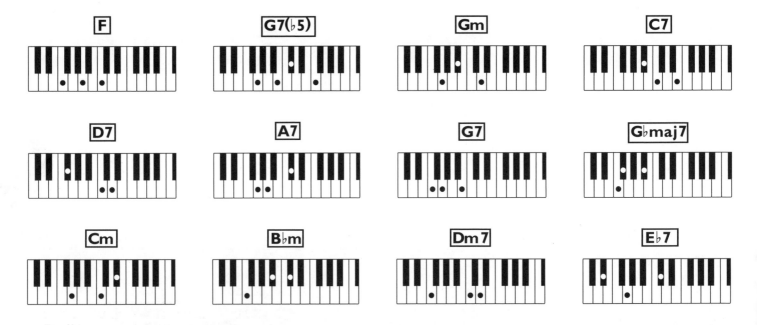

Voice: **Voice Bass/Ooh Split**

Rhythm: **Bossa Nova**

Tempo: ♩ = 128

Love is like a ne - ver end - ing me - lo - dy.____

Po - ets have com - pared it to a sym - pho - ny,____

a sym - pho - ny con - duc - ted by the light - ing of the moon,

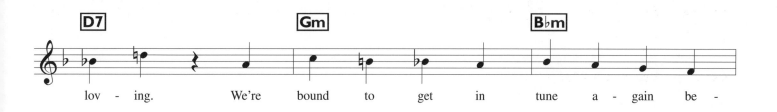

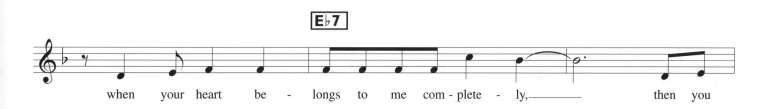

DOS GARDENIAS

Words & Music by Isolina Carrillo

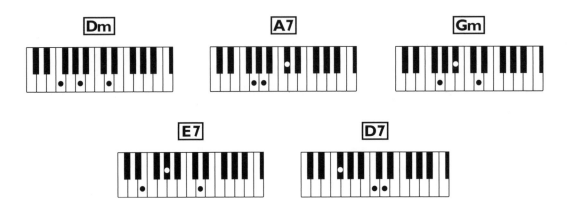

Voice: **Soprano Saxophone**

Rhythm: **Bolero**

Tempo: ♩ = 106

Dos gar-de-nias pa-ra tí, con e-llas quie-ro de-cir. Te

quie-ro, te a-do-ro mi vi-da. _____ Pon-le to-da tu a-ten-

-ción por-que son tu co-ra-zón. Y el mí-o. _____

_____ Dos gar-de-nias pa-ra tí, que ten-drán to-do el ca-lor de un

be - so_____ de e - sos be - sos que te dí y que ja - más en - con - tra -

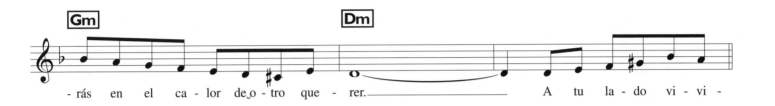

-rás en el ca - lor de o - tro que - rer._____ A tu la - do vi - vi -

-rán y se ha - bla - rán co - mo cuan - do e - stás con - mi - go._____

_____ Y has - ta cre - e - rás, que te di - rán te quie - ro._____

_____ Pe - ro si un a - tar - de - cer las gar - de - nias de mi a - mor se

mue - ren._____ Es por que han a - di - vi - na - do que tu a - mor me ha trai - cio -

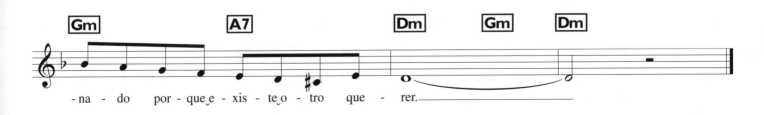

-na - do por que e - xis - te o - tro que - rer._____

THE GIRL FROM IPANEMA
(Garota De Ipanema)

Original Words by Vinicius De Moraes
Music by Antonio Carlos Jobim
English Words by Norman Gimbel

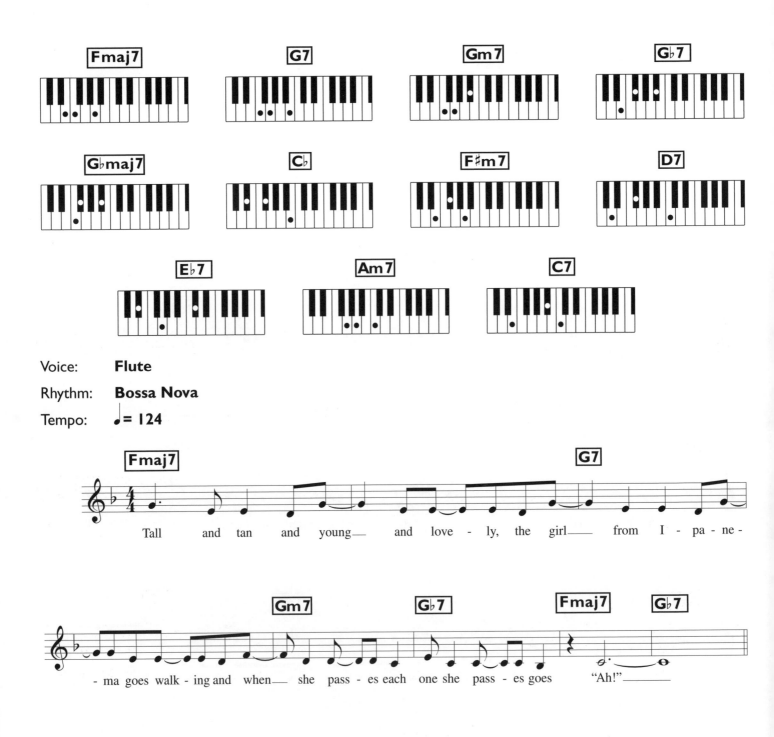

Voice: **Flute**

Rhythm: **Bossa Nova**

Tempo: ♩ = 124

Tall and tan and young and love-ly, the girl from I-pa-ne-ma goes walk-ing and when she pass-es each one she pass-es goes "Ah!"

When she walks she's like a sam-ba that swings so cool and sways so gen-tle that when

16

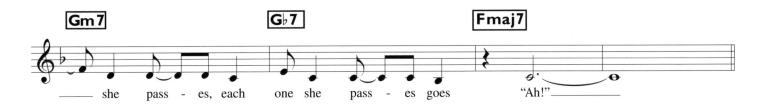

she pass - es, each one she pass - es goes "Ah!" ———

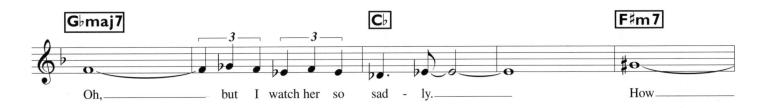

Oh, ——— but I watch her so sad - ly. ——— How ———

—— can I tell her I love her? ——— Yes ——— I would give my heart

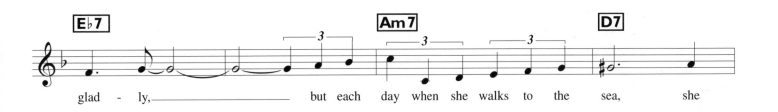

glad - ly, ——— but each day when she walks to the sea, she

looks straight a - head, not at me. Tall and tan and young — and love - ly, the girl —

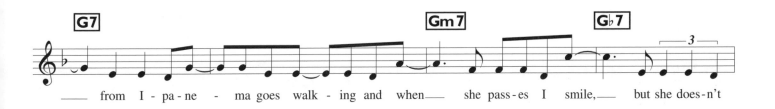

—— from I - pa - ne - ma goes walk - ing and when — she pass - es I smile, — but she does-n't

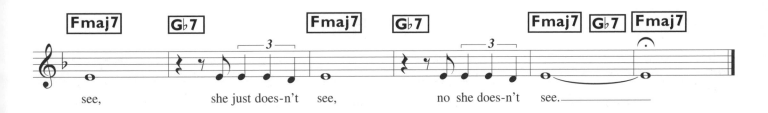

see, she just does-n't see, no she does-n't see. ———

GUAGLIONE

By Giovanni Fanciulli & Nisa
© Copyright 1956 (renewed 1984) Accordo Edizioni Musicali, Milan, Italy.
Eaton Music Limited, 8 West Eaton Place, London SW1
for the United Kingdom, Eire, Australia & New Zealand.
All Rights Reserved. International Copyright Secured.

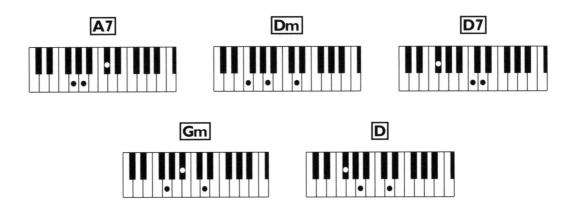

Voice: **Electric Organ**

Rhythm: **Cha Cha**

Tempo: ♩ = 140

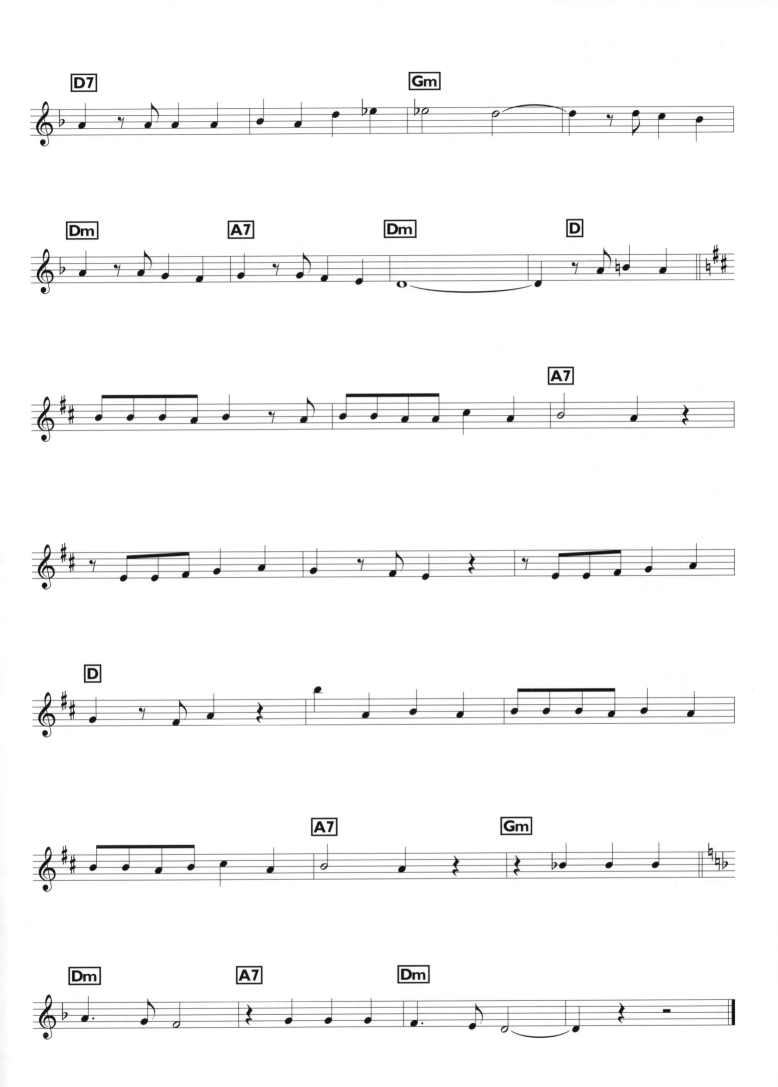

GUANTANAMERA

Lyric Adaptation by Julian Orbon based on a poem by Jose Marti
Music Adaptation by Pete Seeger & Julian Orbon
© Copyright 1963 & 1965 Fall River Music Incorporated, USA.
Harmony Music Limited, 11 Uxbridge Street, London W8 for the British Commonwealth
of Nations (excluding Canada and Australasia) and the Republic of Eire.
All Rights Reserved. International Copyright Secured.

Voice: **12 String Guitar**

Rhythm: **Bolero**

Tempo: ♩ = 122

Lyrics under the staves:

Guan - ta - na - me - ra, gua - ji - ra

Guan - ta - na - me - ra. Guan - ta - na - me -

- ra, gua - ji - ra Guan - ta - na - me - ra. I'm just a

man who is try - ing to do some

good be - fore dy - ing, to ask each

LA BAMBA

Traditional
Adapted & Arranged by Ritchie Valens
© *Copyright 1958 Kemo Music Company, USA.*
Carlin Music Corporation, Iron Bridge House, 3 Bridge Approach, London NW1
for the British Commonwealth (excluding Canada & Australasia), Eire & Israel.
All Rights Reserved. International Copyright Secured.

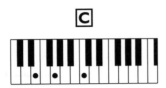 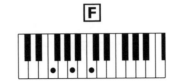 

Voice: **Piano 2**

Rhythm: **Samba**

Tempo: ♩ = 138

Pa - ra bai - lar la bam - - ba,

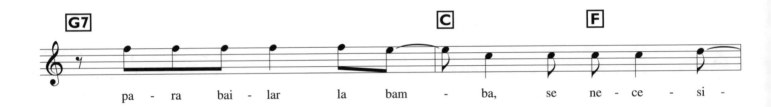

pa - ra bai - lar la bam - ba, se ne - ce - si -

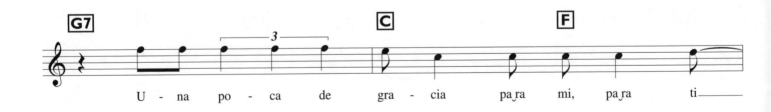

- ta, un po - ca de gra - cia.

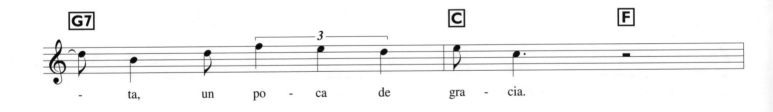

U - na po - ca de gra - cia pa - ra mi, pa - ra ti___

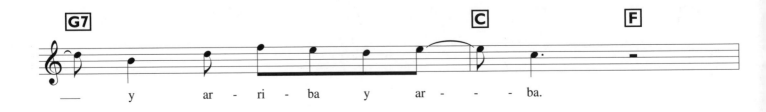

___ y ar - ri - ba y ar - - ba.

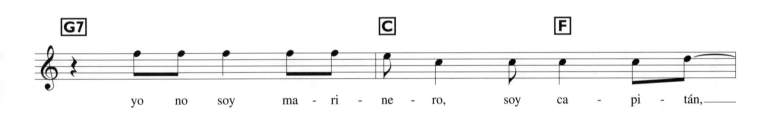

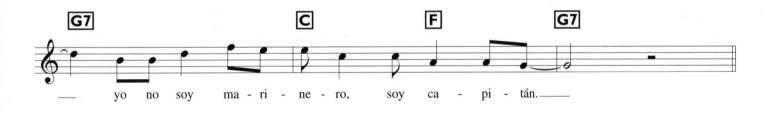

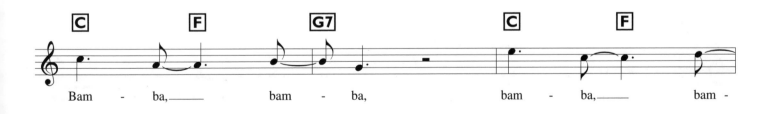

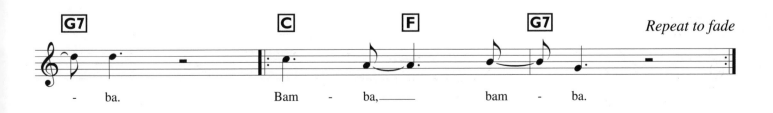

LA CUCARACHA

Traditional

marilaso Dosll 110
allegro

TEX M EX 2:4
mariachi

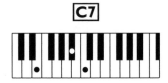

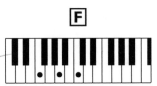

Voice: **Trumpet**

Rhythm: **Rumba**

Tempo: ♩ = 138

La cu - ca - ra - cha, la cu - ca - ra - cha,

run - ning up and down the house. La cu - ca - ra - cha, la cu - ca -

- ra - cha, qui - et as a lit - tle mouse.

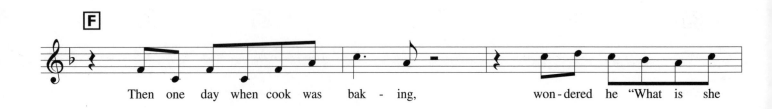

Then one day when cook was bak - ing, won - dered he "What is she

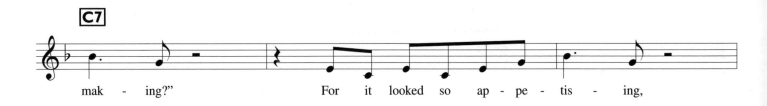

mak - ing?" For it looked so ap - pe - tis - ing,

with the bat-ter slow-ly ris - ing. To the edge he start-ed

skip - ping, then he found that he was slip - ping

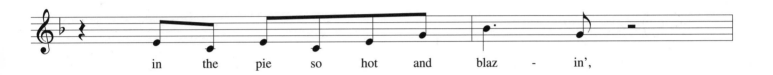

in the pie so hot and blaz - in',

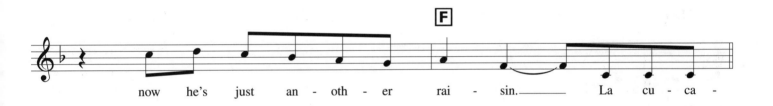

now he's just an - oth - er rai - sin. La cu - ca -

- ra - cha, la cu - ca - ra - cha, just the same as you and

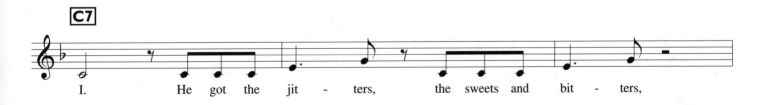

I. He got the jit - ters, the sweets and bit - ters,

lived and loved and said "Good - bye!"

LAMBADA

Words & Music by Ulises Hermosa, Gonzales Hermosa,
Alberto Maravi, Marcia Ferreira & Jose Ari.
Music by Ulises Hermosa & Gonzales Hermosa
© Copyright 1989 EMI Songs, France & Predisa, Mexico.
EMI Music Publishing Limited, 127 Charing Cross Road, London WC2.
All Rights Reserved. International Copyright Secured.

Voice: **Electric Piano 2**

Rhythm: **Lambada**

Tempo: ♩ = 115

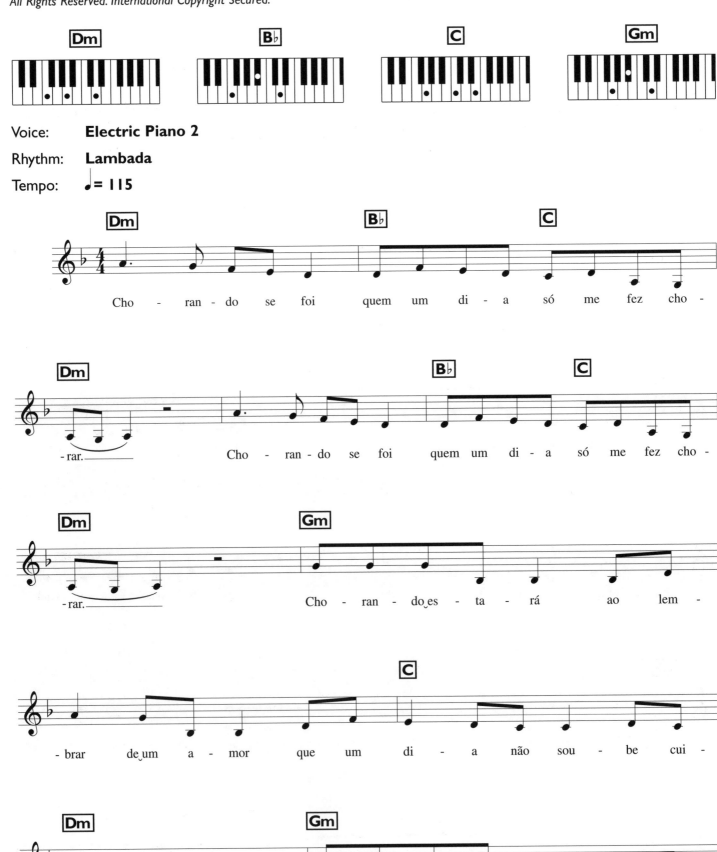

- brar de um a - mor que um di - a não sou - be cui - dar.

A re - cor - da - ção vai es - tar com e - le a - on - de

for. A re - cor - da - ção vai es - tar p'ra sem - pre a - on - de

for. Dan - ça sol e mar guar - da -

- rei no o - lhar o a - mor faz per - der en - con -

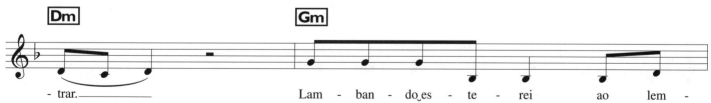

- trar. Lam - ban - do es - te - rei ao lem -

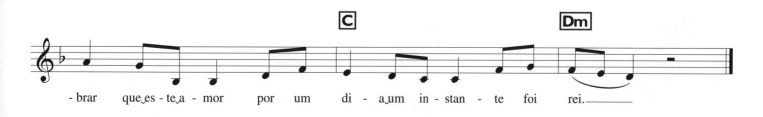

- brar que es - te a - mor por um di - a um in - stan - te foi rei.

LIVIN' LA VIDA LOCA

Words & Music by Desmond Child & Robi Rosa

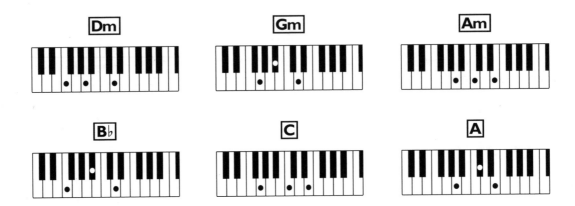

Voice: **Piano 2**

Rhythm: **Samba**

Tempo: ♩ = 88

She's in-to su-per-sti-tion, black cats and voo-doo dolls

and I feel a pre-mo-ni-tion, that girl's gon-na make me fall.

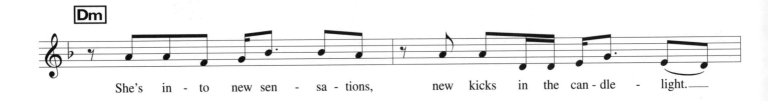

She's in-to new sen-sa-tions, new kicks in the can-dle-light.

She's got a new ad - dic - tion s'full ev - 'ry day and night. She'll make you take your clothes off and go

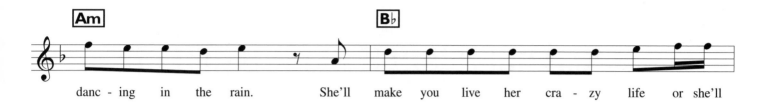

danc - ing in the rain. She'll make you live her cra - zy life or she'll

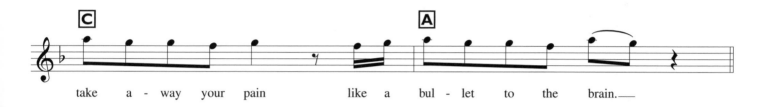

take a - way your pain like a bul - let to the brain.

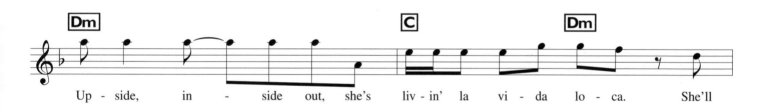

Up - side, in - side out, she's liv - in' la vi - da lo - ca. She'll

push and pull you down, liv - in' la vi - da lo - ca. Her lips are dev - il red and her

skin's the co - lour of mo - cha. She will wear you out, liv - in' la vi - da lo - ca,

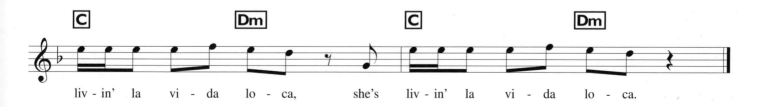

liv - in' la vi - da lo - ca, she's liv - in' la vi - da lo - ca.

MALAGUEÑA

Reggaelón — Dance

English Words by George Brown
Music by Ernesto Lecuona

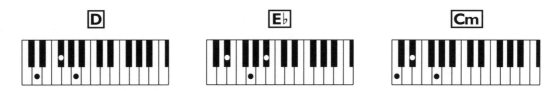

Voice: **Brass Ensemble**

Rhythm: **Tango 2**

Tempo: ♩ = 126

or orchestral Brass
E trumpet. 120

Má - la - ga,_____ where our lips first

met, to the beat_____ of the cas - ta - net. Now I pray____

____ to the skies a - bove, bring him back,_____ please bring back my

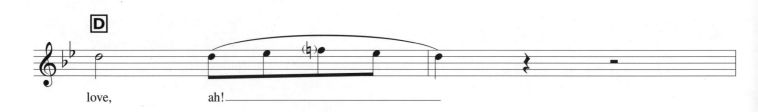

love, ah!_____

Má - la - ga, blue seas____ still e - cho____ his

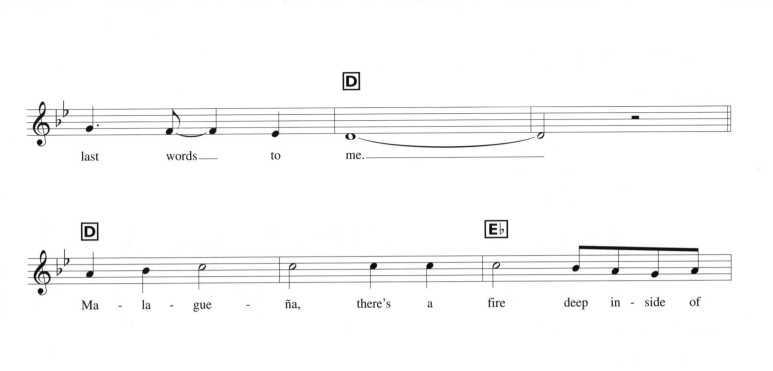

last words —— to me. ——————————

Ma - la - gue - ña, there's a fire deep in - side of

me that must burn, die out, so

I can be free. If no spark

lin - gers with - in when the storm is past, I'll be

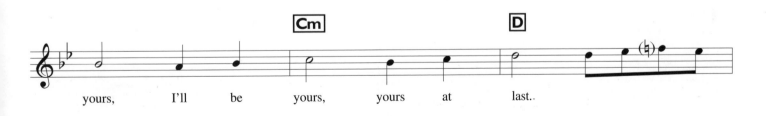

yours, I'll be yours, yours at last.

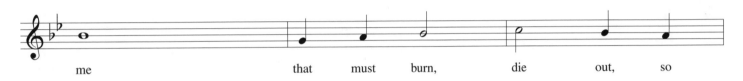

MAMBO No.5 (A LITTLE BIT OF...)

Music by Perez 'Prez' Prado
Words by Lou Bega & Zippy

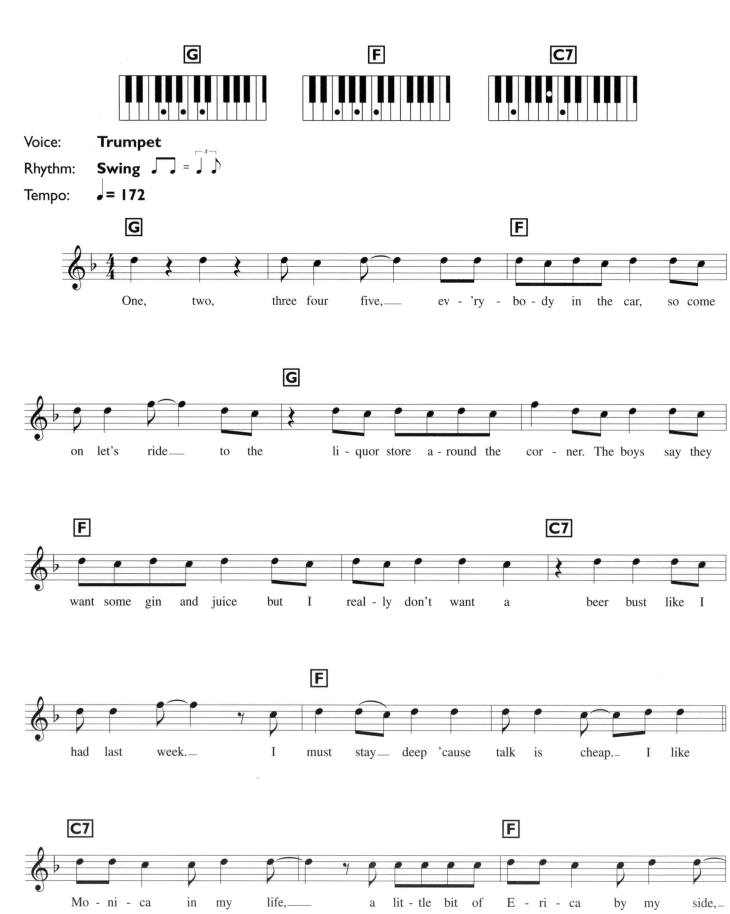

a lit - tle bit of Ri - ta's all I need,____ a lit - tle bit of

Ti - na's what I see.____ A lit - tle bit of San - dra in the sun,____

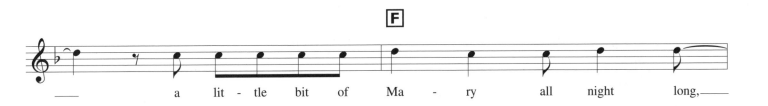

____ a lit - tle bit of Ma - ry all night long,____

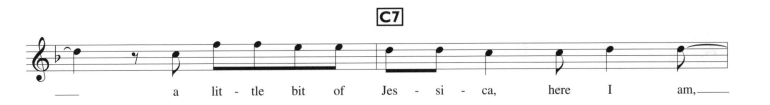

____ a lit - tle bit of Jes - si - ca, here I am,____

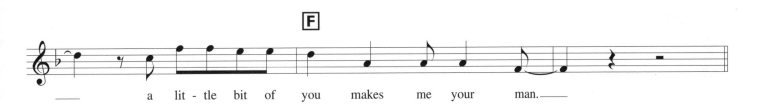

____ a lit - tle bit of you makes me your man.____

MAS QUE NADA

Words & Music by Jorge Ben

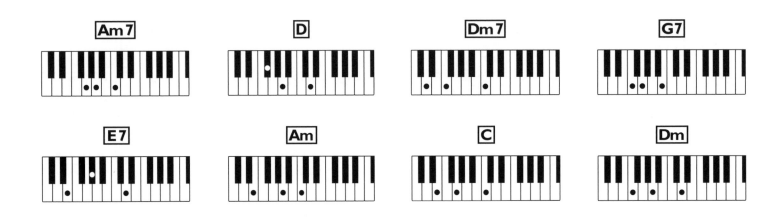

Voice: **Studio Piano**

Rhythm: **Samba**

Tempo: ♩ = 130

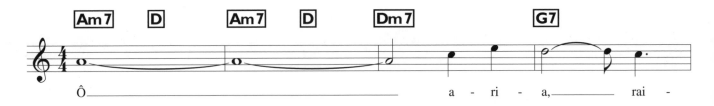

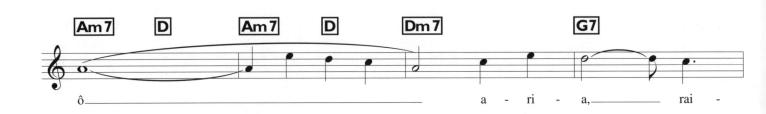

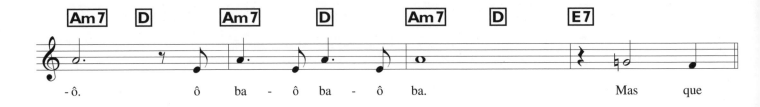

na - da   sa da mi-nha frente que eu quer-o pas - sar.____   Pois o sam-ba es-tá a-ni-ma__

____ do____ o que eu quer-o de____ sam - bar.____   Es - se

sam - ba____ que é mix - to de ma-ra-ca tú.____   é sam-ba de pre-to

ve - lho,____ sam - ba de pre-to tú.____   Mas   que

na-da   um sam-ba co-mo esse tão le-gal,__ vo-cê não vai quer-

-er,   que eu che - gue no____ fi - nal.____   ô

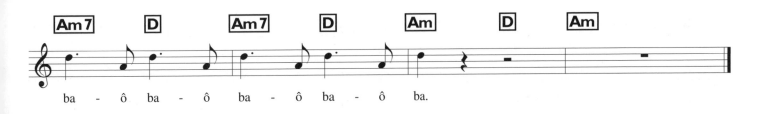

ba - ô ba - ô ba - ô ba - ô ba.

MEDITATION
(Meditaçao)

Original Words by Newton Mendonca
Music by Antonio Carlos Jobim
English Words by Norman Gimbel

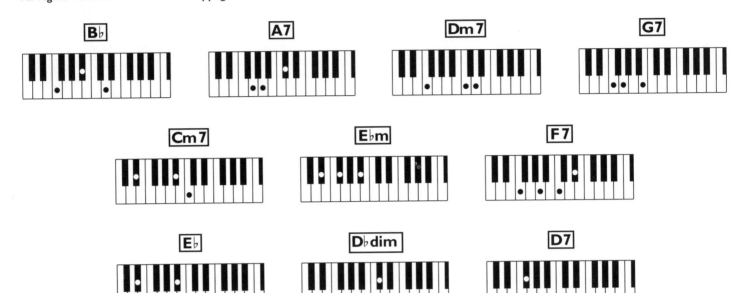

Voice: **Trumpet**

Rhythm: **Bossa Nova**

Tempo: ♩ = 84

In _____ my lon - li - ness, _____ when you've gone and I'm all

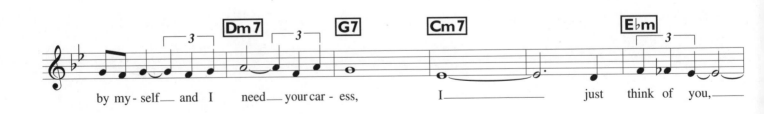

by my - self ___ and I need ___ your car - ess, I _____ just think of you, ___

_____ and the thought of you hold-ing me near makes the lone - li - ness soon dis - sa - pear.

Though _____ you're far a - way, _____ I have on - ly to close my

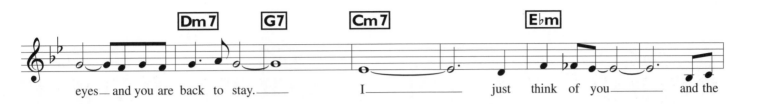

eyes ___ and you are back to stay. _____ I _____ just think of you _____ and the

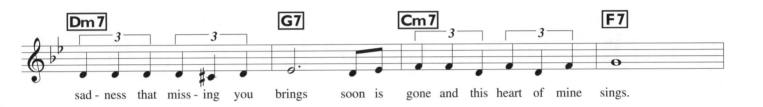

sad - ness that miss - ing you brings soon is gone and this heart of mine sings.

Yes _____ I love you so _____ and that for me is all I need to know.

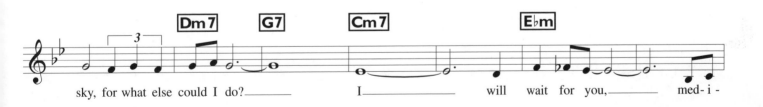

_____ I _____ will wait for you _____ 'til the sun falls from out of the

sky, for what else could I do? _____ I _____ will wait for you, _____ med - i -

-ta - ting how sweet life will be when you come back to me. _____

ONE NOTE SAMBA
(Samba De Uma Nota Só)

Original Words by Newton Mendonca
Music by Antonio Carlos Jobim
English Words by Jon Hendricks

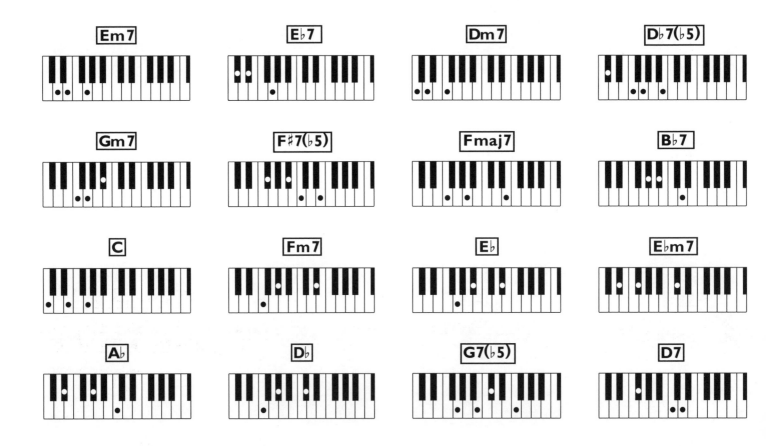

Voice: **Voice Bass/Ooh Split**

Rhythm: **Bossa Nova**

Tempo: ♩ = 124

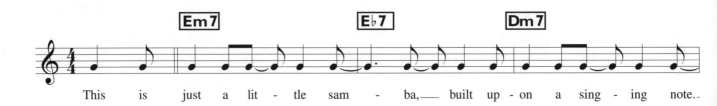

This is just a lit - tle sam - ba,— built up - on a sing - ing note.

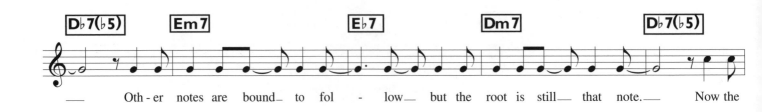

__ Oth - er notes are bound_ to fol - low_ but the root is still__ that note.__ Now the

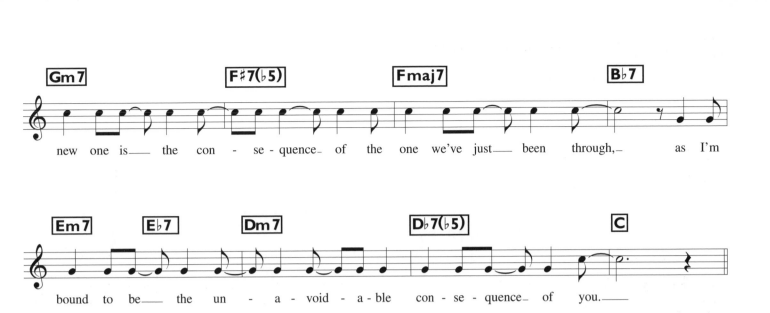

OYE COMO VA

Words & Music by Tito Puente

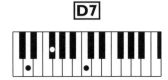

Voice: **Piano**

Rhythm: **Lambada**

Tempo: ♩ = 128

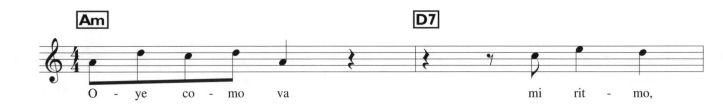

O - ye co - mo va   mi rit - mo,

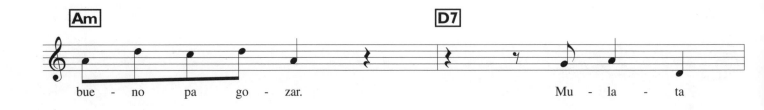

bue - no pa go - zar.   Mu - la - ta

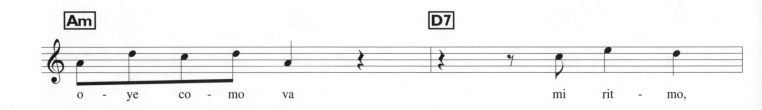

o - ye co - mo va   mi rit - mo,

bue - no pa go - zar.   Mu - la - ta

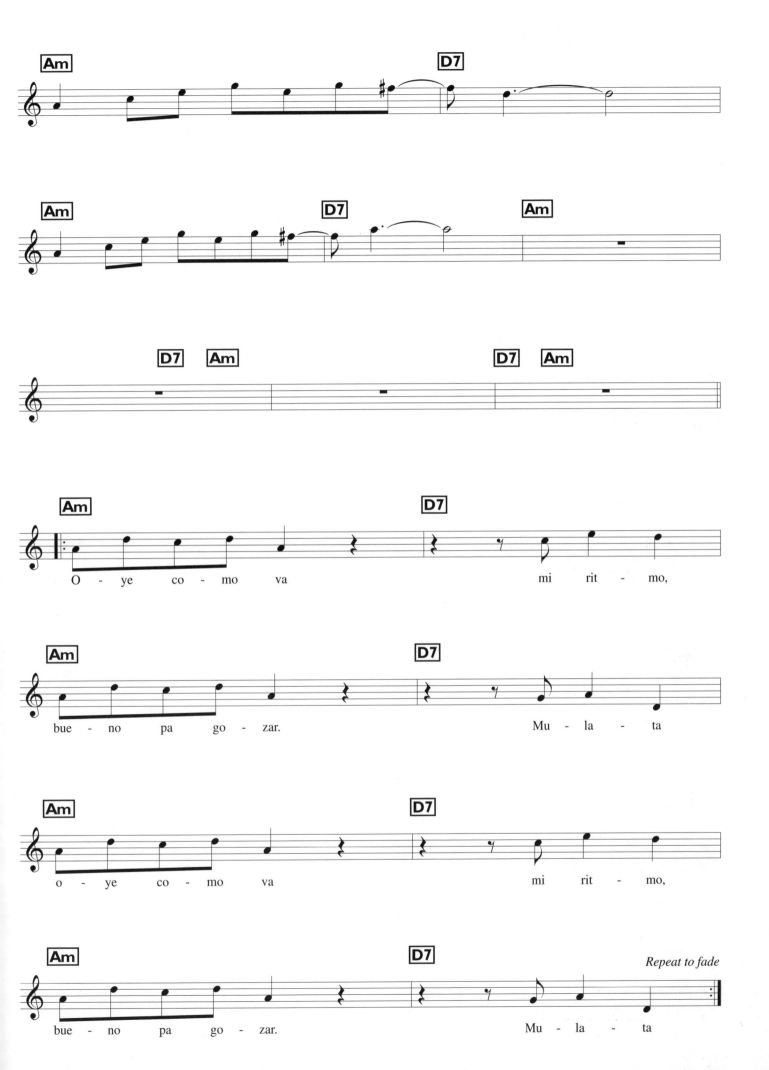

SWAY
(Quien Sera)

Original Words & Music by Pablo Beltran Ruiz
English Words by Norman Gimbel

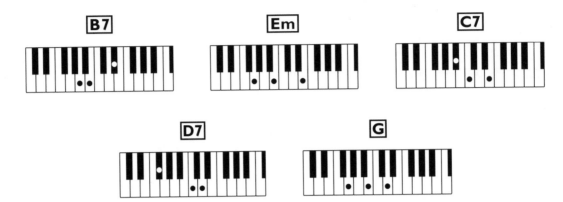

Voice: **Strings/Trumpet**

Rhythm: **Ska**

Tempo: ♩= 132

When ca-lyp-so rhy-thms start to play,— dance with me,—

make me sway.— Like the la-zy o-cean hugs the shore,—

hold me close,— sway me more.— Like a flow-er bend-ing

in the breeze,— bend with me,— sway with ease.—

When we dance you have a way with me, stay with me, sway with me.

Oth - er dan - cers may be on the floor, I got eyes dear, to

see on - ly you. On - ly you have that ma - gic tech - nique,

when we sway I grow weak. I can hear the sound of

vi - o - lins, long be - fore it be - gins.

Make me thrill as on - ly you know how, sway me smooth,

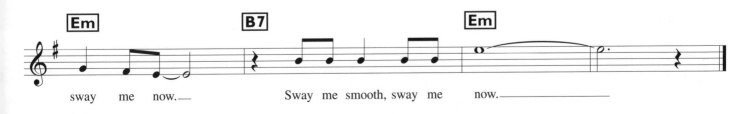

sway me now. Sway me smooth, sway me now.

TEQUILA

Words & Music by Chuck Rio

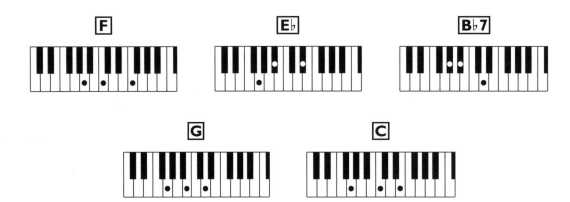

Voice: **Trumpet**

Rhythm: **Bosa Nova**

Tempo: ♩ = 140

VAYA CON DIOS

Words & Music by Larry Russell, Inez James & Buddy Pepper

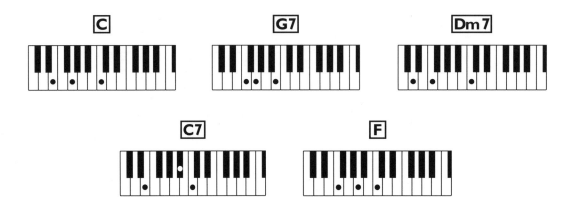

Voice:	**12 String Guitar**
Rhythm:	**Rock Waltz**
Tempo:	♩ = 120

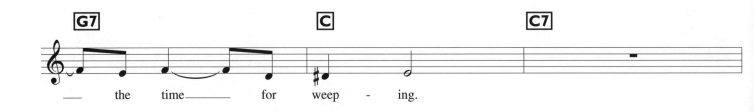

Now the ha - ci - en - da's dark, _____ the town _____ is

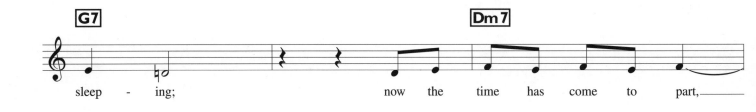

sleep - ing; now the time has come to part, _____

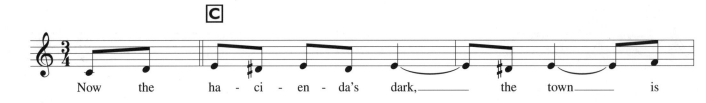

_____ the time _____ for weep - ing.

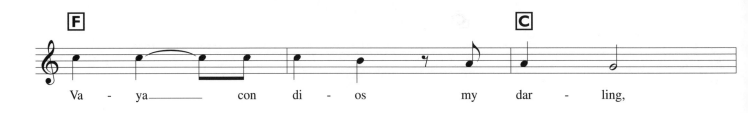

Va - ya _____ con di - os my dar - ling,

may God_____ be with you, my

love. Now the vil - lage mis - sion bells_____

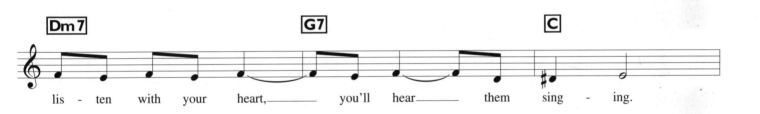

_____ are soft - - ly ring - ing; if you

lis - ten with your heart,_____ you'll hear_____ them sing - ing.

Va - ya_____ con di - os my

dar - ling, may God_____ be

with you, my love.

EASIEST KEYBOARD COLLECTION

Easy-to-play melody line arrangements for all keyboards with chord symbols and lyrics. Suggested registration, rhythm and tempo are included for each song together with keyboard diagrams showing left-hand chord voicings used.

 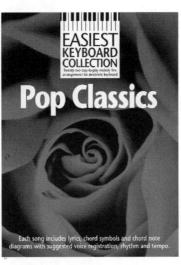 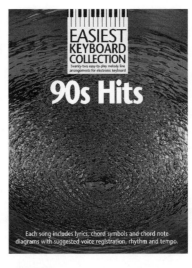 

Showstoppers
Consider Yourself (Oliver!), Do You Hear The People Sing? (Les Misérables), I Know Him So Well (Chess), Maria (West Side Story), Smoke Gets In Your Eyes (Roberta) and 17 more big stage hits.
Order No. AM944218

Pop Classics
A Whiter Shade Of Pale (Procol Harum), Bridge Over Troubled Water (Simon & Garfunkel), Crocodile Rock (Elton John) and 19 more classic hit songs, including Hey Jude (The Beatles), Imagine (John Lennon), and Massachusetts (The Bee Gees).
Order No. AM944196

90s Hits
Over 20 of the greatest hits of the 1990s, including Always (Bon Jovi), Fields Of Gold (Sting), Have I Told You Lately (Rod Stewart), One Sweet Day (Mariah Carey), Say You'll Be There (Spice Girls), and Wonderwall (Oasis).
Order No. AM944229

Abba
A great collection of 22 Abba hit songs. Includes: Dancing Queen, Fernando, I Have A Dream, Mamma Mia, Super Trouper, Take A Chance On Me, Thank You For The Music, The Winner Takes It All, and Waterloo.
Order No. AM959860

Also available...

Ballads, Order No. AM952116	**The Corrs**, Order No. AM959849
The Beatles, Order No. NO90686	**Elton John**, Order No. AM958320
Boyzone, Order No. AM958331	**Film Themes**, Order No. AM952050
Broadway, Order No. AM952127	**Hits of the 90s,** Order No. AM955780
Celine Dion, Order No. AM959850	**Jazz Classics**, Order No. AM952061
Chart Hits, Order No. AM952083	**Love Songs**, Order No. AM950708
Christmas, Order No. AM952105	**Pop Hits**, Order No. AM952072
Classic Blues, Order No. AM950697	**60s Hits**, Order No. AM955768
Classics, Order No. AM952094	**80s Hits**, Order No. AM955779

...plus many more!